James

chalos

CaW

Sam the Referee

Janet and Allan Ahlberg

Collins

One day Sam has to look after five little children
and a big dog.

The children's names are Henry, Jim, Jennifer,

Brian and Mary.

The dog's name is Barker.

Sam says, "We will play football.
Henry, Jim and Jennifer will be one team.
Brian, Mary and Barker will be the other team.
These teddies and dolls will be the goal-posts.
I will be the referee."

Then Stanley and Eric arrive.

They ask Sam what he is doing. Sam tells them.
"Good," says Eric, "we'll be the linesmen."
"Yes," Stanley says, "and we'll use our
handkerchiefs as flags."

So Sam blows his whistle and the game begins.

Henry passes to Jim.
Jim picks up the ball and runs off with it.
"Handball!" says Sam, and he blows his whistle.

Brian takes the free kick, and misses the ball.

Brian takes another free kick
and Mary scores a brilliant goal.

"1–0," says Sam, and he writes the score
in his note-book.

Fred, Ambrose and Trevor arrive.

They ask Sam what he is doing. Sam tells them.
"We'll watch," says Fred.
"Yes," Ambrose says, "we'll be the crowd."

The game begins again. Henry passes to Jim.
Jim puts the ball up his jumper.
"Stop that!" says Sam, and he writes Jim's name
in his note-book.

"Boo!" says the crowd.

Mary takes her teddy for a walk.
"Put that goal-post back!" says Sam.
"No!" says Mary.
Sam writes Mary's name in his note-book.

The crowd shout rude things about the referee.

A cat walks across the pitch.

Barker chases the cat.
"Get back in goal you bad dog!" says Sam.
"Woof!" says Barker.
Sam writes Barker's name in his note-book.

The crowd sing rude songs about the referee.

Brian and Henry start fighting for the ball,
and Jennifer cries for her mummy.
"Stop it!" says Sam. "All of you stop it!"
Sam writes everybody's name in his note-book.

Barker bites the ball.
"Right," says Sam, "that's it." He blows his whistle.
"You are all sent off!"

Then Tom, Bruce, Oliver, Walter and
Norman arrive. They ask Sam what he is doing.

"I'm going mad!" says Sam.

He blows his whistle again.
The crowd rush onto the pitch.
The linesmen wave their flags.
Barker starts barking, Jennifer keeps crying,
all the others shout and cheer.
The game is over.

Other books about the Brick Street Boys:

Here are the Brick Street Boys
A Place to Play
Fred's Dream
The Great Marathon Football Match

First published 1975
This edition 1986
© Janet and Allan Ahlberg 1975

ISBN 0 00 138012–5

Printed in Italy by   New Interlitho, Milan